Piano Exam Pieces

ABRSM Grade 2

Selected from the 2019 & 2020 syllabus

Date of exam

Contents

page

LIST A

LIST B

LIST C

Editor for ABRSM: Richard Jones

Other pieces for Grade 2

LIST A

4 **Clementi** Arietta in F (from *An Introduction to the Art of Playing on the Pianoforte*). *Clementi: The First Book for Young Pianists* (Alfred)

5 **Handel** Air (Hornpipe) in D minor, HWV 461. *Handel: Easy Piano Pieces and Dances* (Bärenreiter)

6 **Haydn** Allegro (4th movt from *Sonata in G*, Hob. XVI:8). *Haydn: Selected Keyboard Sonatas, Book 1* (ABRSM)

LIST B

4 **Beethoven** Nel cor più, arr. Fly. *With the Immortals* (Forsyth)

5 **Gurlitt** Night Journey (No. 65 from *The First Steps of the Young Pianist*, Op. 82). *Music Through Time, Piano Book 1* (OUP)

6 **Somervell** Plaintive Waltz (from *Holiday Pictures*). *A Romantic Sketchbook for Piano, Book 1* (ABRSM)

LIST C

4 **Gillock** A Memory of Paris. *Gillock: Accents Around the World* (Willis)

5 **Saint-Saëns** Royal March of the Lion (from *The Carnival of the Animals*), arr. Litten. *Piano Mix 1* (ABRSM)

6 **Pam Wedgwood** Lazy Days: No. 7 from *Up-Grade! Piano Grades 1–2* (Faber)

First published in 2018 by ABRSM (Publishing) Ltd,
a wholly owned subsidiary of ABRSM, 4 London Wall Place,
London EC2Y 5AU, United Kingdom

Distributed worldwide by Oxford University Press

Music origination by Julia Bovee
Cover by Kate Benjamin & Andy Potts, with thanks to Brighton College
Printed in England by Halstan & Co. Ltd, Amersham, Bucks.,
on materials from sustainable sources.
Reprinted in 2018

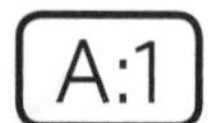

Lesson in C

No. 10 from *Die ersten 12 Lektionen*, Op. 125

Edited by Howard Ferguson

Anton Diabelli
(1781–1858)

The Austrian musician Anton Diabelli settled in Vienna as a music teacher and composer. In 1818 he established a music publishing firm in the city, becoming Schubert's first and chief publisher. In the following year, he sent a waltz theme to all the leading Austrian composers, asking them to write a variation on it. This resulted in one of Beethoven's greatest piano compositions, the so-called Diabelli Variations, Op. 120 (1823).

In the 'Lesson in C', note the contrasting theme in the dominant key at bb. 17–24, which is just as charming as the original theme.

Source: *Die ersten 12 Lektionen, Op. 125* (Vienna: Diabelli, 1830). Some phrase marks and dynamics have been added by the editor.

17
f
legato

21
p

25
mf

29
cresc.
sf
f

A:2

Musette in D

BWV Anh. II 126

Anon.

This piece, generally thought to be by one of J. S. Bach's sons, is found in a little manuscript keyboard book, called 'Clavierbüchlein' (Little Keyboard Book), that Bach dedicated to his wife Anna Magdalena in 1725. This little anthology gives a fascinating glimpse of the music-making that took place in the Bach family's Leipzig home.

The musette is an 18th-century dance movement in pastoral style, with a drone bass that imitates the small French bagpipe known as a 'musette'. This explains the pedal bass that runs through much of this musette.

Source: Staatsbibliothek zu Berlin, Preussischer Kulturbesitz, Mus. ms. Bach P225. All dynamics, slurs and staccatos are editorial suggestions only.

Adapted from J. S. Bach et al.: *The Anna Magdalena Bach Book of 1725*, edited by Richard Jones (ABRSM)

Gigue in the English Style

Gigue à l'Angloise

A:3

Sixth movement from Partita in G, TWV 32:1

G. P. Telemann
(1681–1767)

French and Italian forms of the dance type known as gigue were common in Telemann's day, but here he attempts a 'Gigue in the English Style', to quote the title – an imitation of the older English 'jig'.

Georg Philipp Telemann, an immensely prolific German composer, was city music director at Frankfurt (1712–21), then at Hamburg (1721–67). As a composer, he was versatile enough to turn his hand to all the different styles and genres of his day.

Source: *Der getreue Music-Meister* (Hamburg, 1728). All dynamics and slurs are editorial suggestions only.

Adapted from *Baroque Keyboard Pieces*, Book I, edited by Richard Jones (ABRSM)

B:1

Arabesque

No. 2 from *25 études faciles et progressives*, Op. 100

J. F. F. Burgmüller
(1806–74)

Johann Friedrich Franz Burgmüller, German by birth, settled in Paris after 1832. There he became popular as a pianist and composer, improvising hundreds of salon pieces and composing much piano music for teaching purposes. Many of his short piano pieces have programmatic titles.

An *arabesque* is an ornament found in Arabic art, so in music it refers to decorative writing. In this piece, the arabesque is the quick, short, light semiquaver figure that dominates the right hand of the outer sections (bb. 3 and 19) and the left hand of the middle section (b. 11). Although the composer's metronome mark is ♩ = 152, students may prefer a more relaxed tempo, for example ♩ = 116.

Source: *25 études faciles et progressives, Op. 100* (London: Schott, 1854). The original title is 'L'arabesque'. The dynamic in b. 7 is editorial, as are the directions *sim.* and *stacc.* in bb. 3 and 19.

Adapted from Burgmüller: *25 Easy and Progressive Studies*, Op. 100 (ABRSM)

poco rall.
a tempo
16
dim.
p
stacc.

20
cresc.
p dolce

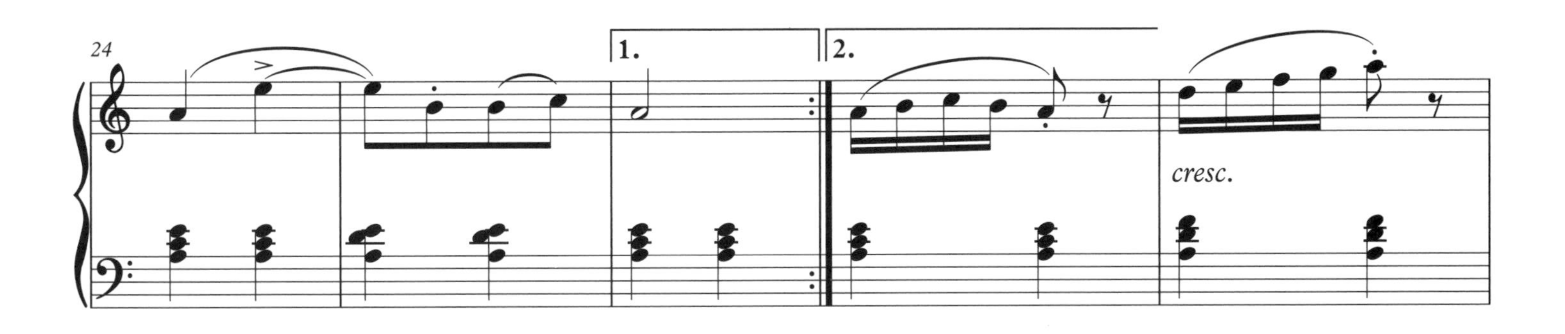
24
1.
2.
cresc.

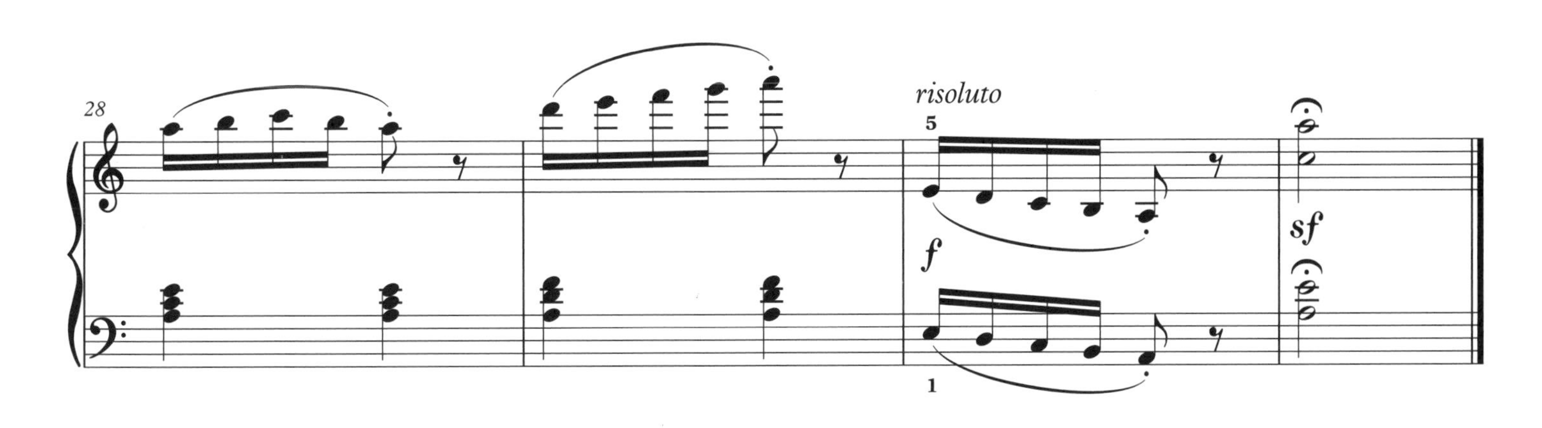
28
risoluto
f
sf

B:2

Waltz

No. 13 from *24 Easy Pieces*, Op. 39

D. B. Kabalevsky
(1904–87)

The Russian composer Dmitry Borisovich Kabalevsky studied piano and composition at the Moscow Conservatory, where he later taught, being appointed professor in 1939. He was active in the field of music education and wrote much music for young people, including the *24 Easy Pieces*, Op. 39, from which this waltz is selected. Here, the sharp contrast between the two hands – sustained, *cantabile* melody in the right; repeated staccato chords in the left – is maintained throughout.

Source: No. 13 from *24 Little Pieces, Op. 39* (1967)

Published in *24 Little Pieces*, Op. 39 (ISMN 979-0-060-034299)

Lazy Bear

B:3

from *Piano Sketches*, Book 1

Vitalij Neugasimov
(born 1978)

Neugasimov's *Piano Sketches*, from which this piece is selected, is a short series of piano miniatures that cover a range of musical styles. In this piece, he paints a picture of a lazy bear: the left-hand melody is at very low pitch, particularly in the major-mode middle section (bb. 9–16).

Vitalij Neugasimov was born in Vilnius, capital of Lithuania, in 1978. He studied piano, organ and music education at the Lithuanian Music Academy, graduating in 2004. He is now active as a music teacher, composer, arranger, conductor and accompanist.

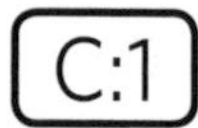

Dusty Blue

from *Paint Box*

June Armstrong
(born 1951)

This piece is selected from June Armstrong's *Paint Box: Very First Concert Pieces for Piano*, where the pieces are organized by colour. The title 'Dusty Blue' is given to a piece in blues style: this applies not only to the character of its right-hand melody, but also to the twelve-bar blues bass and chords that underpin it in the left hand.

The composer has written: 'Keep the left hand very solid and not too fast. You can finger this 5 1, 5 1, etc. or 5 2, 5 1. Make the final *ritenuto* really slow up at the end to give a very bluesy feel.' No dynamics are given, but she says: 'Choose your own and experiment to find out what works best.'

Ja-Da

Arranged by Nikki Iles

Bob Carleton
(c.1894–1956)

Bob Carleton was an American jazz pianist and composer who wrote over 500 songs, including the 1918 hit 'Ja-Da'. This song became a jazz standard and was performed by many artists and bands, including The Original New Orleans Jazz Band, Frank Sinatra and Oscar Peterson.

'Ja-Da' featured in the Tom and Jerry cartoon Trap Happy (1946), where it was heard when Butch the exterminator cat arrives to rid the house of Jerry the mouse. Naturally, he fails!

Reproduced from *Piano Mix 1*, compiled and edited by David Blackwell (ABRSM)

Little Waltz

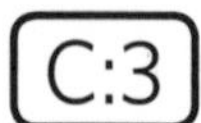

Petite valse

from *Lazy Days*

Brian Chapple
(born 1945)

'Petite valse' is French for 'little waltz'. The *cantabile* melody in triple time, accompanied by repeated chords on the second and third beats, is characteristic of this type of dance.

The English composer Brian Chapple studied composition with Lennox Berkeley and piano with Harry Isaacs at the Royal Academy of Music, London. He has written a wide variety of music, including three small books of piano pieces for his pupils: *In the Pink*, *On the Cool Side*, and *Lazy Days* from which this piece is selected.